Yada Yada Hi Dharmasya Glanir Bhavati Bharata
Abhyuttanam Adharmasya Tadatnaman Srjamy Aham

Whenever and wherever a decline of righteousness and a
predominance of unrighteousness prevail; at that time I manifest
Myself personally, O descendant of Bharata

Sri Krishna to Arjuna, Bhagvad Gita, Chapter 4, Verse 7

Published in 2012 by

anJana
publishing

www.ammatellme.com

27, Strawberry Hill, 8 Plunketts Road, The Peak, Hong Kong

ISBN:978-988-15028-3-4

Designed by Jump Web Services Ltd.
Production by Macmillan Production (Asia) Ltd.
Tracking Code CP-07/12
Printed in Guangdong Province China
This book is printed on paper made from well-managed sustainable forest sources.

Amma, Tell Me About Krishna!

Written by
Bhakti Mathur

Illustrated by
Maulshree Somani

One by one the boys climbed on each other
Till the pyramid they formed reached the top,
All the way up to the temple's ceiling,
Where there hung a small earthen butter-pot.

And then it was Klaka's turn!
Up, up and up he clambered.
A mighty swing with the stick in his hand,
And there! The butter-pot was shattered.

The temple erupted with shouts of joy,
For this was the climax of the day.
They had all gathered to celebrate Janamashtami,
The festival that marks Krishna's birthday.

Klaka had arrived at the temple quite early
With his brother Kiki, that day.
There was so much that they had to do:
A bit of work, but mostly play!

Finally the time arrived, and
The clock's hands moved to strike midnight.
This was the moment of Krishna's birth!
All rejoiced and danced in delight.

After the festivities were over,

As Amma tucked Klaka into bed,

"I'm not sleepy at all!

Amma, tell me about Krishna!" he said.

"All right, then listen carefully," said Amma.
"My grandmother used to tell me this story
About how Krishna was born,
And of his great deeds, and rise to glory.

Janam means birth,
And Ashtami means eight:
As Krishna was born on the monsoon's eighth day,
It is Janamashtami, which we celebrate.

A long, long time ago, terror had come
To the once-great kingdom of Mathura,
Ever since evil Kansa usurped the crown
From his father, the noble King Ugrasena.

There was fear everywhere,
Destruction, death and pain.
No good citizen was safe
Under wicked Kansa's evil reign.

Desperate, the people turned to Lord Vishnu,
And prayed for Kansa's rule to end.
Vishnu granted their prayer and said,
"To end his rule, to earth I will descend."

Soon after, when Kansa's sister,
The beautiful and good Devaki,
Wedded the noble king Vasudev,
A voice from the sky pronounced this prophecy.

"Listen, O wicked Kansa,
Know now that your end is near.
The eighth child of Devaki will cause your demise
And rid Mathura's people of their fear."

On hearing this, Kansa seized Devaki,
And drew his sword to kill her.
"My end will never come," he said,
"If I kill you now, my little sister."

Vasudev pleaded with him.
"Kansa, spare your sister's life," he said.
"I promise we will hand you our children;
Do with them what you please, instead."

Kansa agreed, but had Devaki and Vasudev
Chained and locked in a deep dark cell.
One by one he killed their sons;
It was a time of horror and hell.

Finally, Devaki's eighth child arrived
On a strange and magical night,
Dark and stormy, yet the wind sang softly
As though to welcome a ray of light.

A beautiful baby boy arrived
At the very stroke of midnight.
With dark blue skin and lovely big eyes,
He lit the dark prison with his godly light.

Then a heavenly voice announced,
"Vasudev, your sorrows are at an end.
Take this child across the Yamuna River,
To Gokul, where lives Nand, your friend."

Lo and behold, Vasudev's chains came undone
And the prison door opened on its own stead.
The guards fell into a deep sleep;
A magical light marked the path ahead.

In wonder, Vasudev picked up the baby
And walked out into the stormy night.
He reached the Yamuna, but how could he cross?
How could he follow the magical light?

He held the baby up over his head,
Bravely stepped in the water, then had a shock.
For suddenly, the Yamuna parted,
Revealing a path on which he could walk.

Then from the river emerged a huge serpent -
The heavenly Shesh Naag, whose giant head
Formed an umbrella over father and son,
As through the parted Yamuna, they did tread.

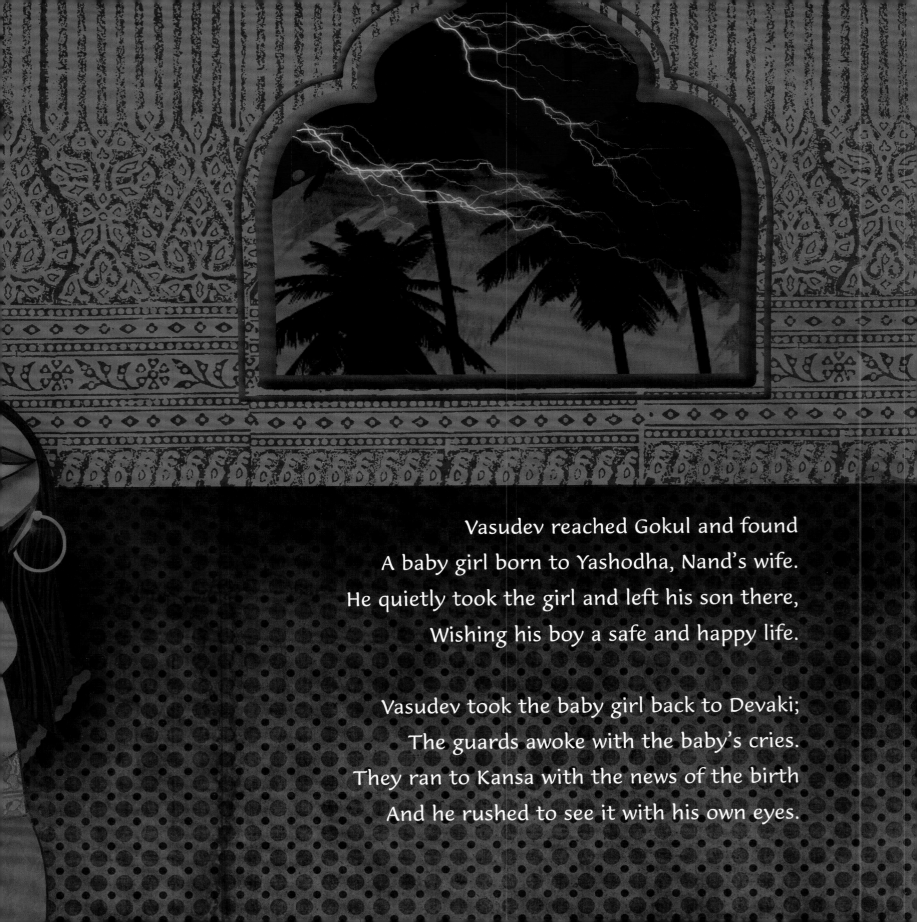

Vasudev reached Gokul and found
A baby girl born to Yashodha, Nand's wife.
He quietly took the girl and left his son there,
Wishing his boy a safe and happy life.

Vasudev took the baby girl back to Devaki;
The guards awoke with the baby's cries.
They ran to Kansa with the news of the birth
And he rushed to see it with his own eyes.

He snatched the baby from Devaki, and
Flung her against the wall with a screech.
But the baby instead flew out of his grip,
Floating up in the air and out of his reach.

The baby was really the Goddess Yogamaya,
And as she flew away, she laughed and said,
"O Kansa, your nemesis is alive and well.
Nothing can save you, you will soon be dead."

Filled with dread, Kansa ordered his soldiers
To seek out all newborns in Mathura.
Even though they searched far and wide,
The soldiers could never harm Krishna.

When Yashodha awoke the next morning,
She thought the sleeping baby was her son.
Seeing his blue skin, she named him Krishna,
Which means blue like a cloud, attracting everyone!

The villagers in Gokul were delighted that
A son was born to Nand and Yashodha.
They danced and celebrated with joy
The arrival of baby Krishna.

So that, my dear Klaka,
Is how Krishna came to be.
Another night I'll tell you the story
Of how he brought Kansa to his knees."